ACTION
CHARADES

ADULT CHARADES

With research by Abi McMahon

Illustrations © Shutterstock

Summersdale Publishers Ltd
46 West Street
Chichester
West Sussex
PO19 1RP
UK

www.summersdale.com

Printed and bound in Malta

ISBN: 978-1-84953-943-2

Substantial discounts on bulk quantities of Summersdale books are available to corporations, professional associations and other organisations. For details contact Nicky Douglas by telephone: +44 (0) 1243 756902, fax: +44 (0) 1243 786300 or email: nicky@summersdale.com.

NAUGHTY IDEAS FOR YOUR FAVOURITE PARTY GAME

SADIE CAYMAN

summersdale

CONTENTS

HOW TO PLAY

→ The players divide into two teams of at least two members.

→ Decide which team will go first. One member of the team flicks through this book, stopping and placing a finger on a page at random to decide their charade. They should keep their choice a secret from the remainder of their team, the 'guessers'.

→ They then have one minute (use the timer on your phone, or an egg timer if you have one) to attempt to act it out. The actor must not make any sounds (no talking, singing or humming). Lip movements are prohibited, and they can't point at any objects around them to help the guessers. Drawing letters in the air is also not allowed. The guessers attempt to work out the word or phrase within the time limit. They can ask questions, but only non-verbal responses are allowed, such as nodding the head.

→ If the guessers get the right answer, their team gets a point; if they haven't guessed it when the time limit expires, the other team gets a point.

→ The teams alternate until each member has had an opportunity to be the mimer.

→ For a quick-fire version of the game, increase the time to two or three minutes and see how many correct answers one team can guess within the limit.

→ Alternatively, teams can take it in turns to pick their favourite suggestions and write them on pieces of paper to put into a hat. The mimers then pick a piece of paper at random at the start of their go.

→ Due to the naughty nature of some of the suggestions, the actor might need the assistance of someone else in their team to act something out fully, but it's important the guest mimer doesn't know what the answer is – they can only be used as a prop, acting 'blind'.

→ Symbols are traditionally used to indicate whether what you're about to act out represents the whole answer in one go (making a circle between both of your hands), the total number of words in the answer (holding up the relevant number of fingers), the specific word you're acting out (holding up the number of fingers to indicate which position the word is in, in the answer) and the number of syllables in the word you're currently acting out (holding the number of fingers against your forearm). Here are some other signs that may come in useful:

Small word: Hold up your thumb and forefinger close together to indicate that you're miming a short word (typically 'and', 'to', 'the', etc.)

Chop the word: If a player is guessing a longer version of the word you're miming (for instance, 'running' instead of 'run'), you should bring the side of one hand down on the back of the other in a chopping motion to tell them to cut it down.

Extend the word: To indicate that they've got part of the word correct, but they need a longer version of the word (e.g. they've guessed 'cream', and you need them to say 'creamy'), hold up your two forefingers and move them apart from each other.

Sounds like: Tug your ear to indicate that you're going to act out a word that rhymes with the word in the answer.

You're on the wrong track: Wave your hands, palms down, away from one another in a 'cease' gesture, to tell the guessers that they're guessing along the wrong lines.

You're on the right track: Wave your hands towards yourself, as if you were encouraging them to come closer, to indicate that they're getting there.

Correct!: Touch your nose, while pointing with your other hand at the guesser, makes it clear that their suggestion was on the money.

ADULT CHARADES USES THE FOLLOWING CATEGORIES:

→ **Films:** hold one hand up to your eye as if looking through a camera lens, the other hand cranking like an old-fashioned movie camera

→ **Cocktails:** mime taking a drink

→ **Books:** hold out your hands together in front of you, then open them like a book

→ **Plays and musicals:** go down on one knee and hold your arms out in a flamboyant gesture (think Shakespeare)

→ **Songs:** move your hands outwards from your mouth, like an opera singer

→ **TV shows:** describe a small rectangle in the air with your forefingers

→ **Food:** mime eating with a knife and fork

→ **Sports:** act out hitting a ball with a bat

THE FUN RULES

If you want your game of Adult Charades to be even more naughty, pick from these additional rules:

→ Every time your team guesses correctly, the other team takes a drink.

→ Every time your team guesses correctly, someone in the other team has to remove an item of clothing.

→ Every time you guess correctly you 'win' the opportunity to ask a truth or dare of one of your opponents. They have to either answer a question truthfully or perform a naughty act of your choice.

SCORING

When you've finished playing, check how well you've done. For every ten mimes your team acted out, work out how many you guessed correctly:

→ **1–3:** You're little in the amateur league – you need to up your naughtiness and try again. Try wearing sexier underwear next time – or maybe no underwear!

→ **4–6:** Not bad – you have plenty of enthusiasm but you need to work on your technique to give full satisfaction.

→ **7–8:** Hot stuff – your bad girl/boy act is clearly no charade. Encore!

→ **9–10:** Blow me away! You are a real pro at this game. Is there something you're not telling us?

FILMS

Hold one hand up to your eye as if looking through a camera lens, the other hand cranking like an old-fashioned movie camera.

INTRODUCTION

As we grow older it becomes increasingly clear that all the good, clean family films that we loved as children are really rather rude. Of course usually it's not until halfway through a relaxing game of family charades, and your one uncle throwing himself rather too enthusiastically into miming *Free Willy*, that the realisation strikes. Once you've stopped cringing from that mental image, there are plenty of dirty children's movies – such as *Chitty Chitty Bang Bang* and *Willy Wonka and the Chocolate Factory* – to be found in the following pages, to say nothing of all those filthy films for grown-ups. By which I mean thrillers such as *Deep Impact*, of course.

Die Hard

. . . .

Up

. . . .

The Full Monty

. . . .

Tristram Shandy:
A Cock and Bull Story

. . . .

Lethal Weapon

. . . .

The Naked Gun

. . . .

Dirty Harry

. . . .

Fun with Dick and Jane

Forrest Gump

· · · · · · · · · · · · · · · · · · ·

Ghost Rider

· · · · · · · · · · · · · · · · · · ·

Meet the Fockers

· · · · · · · · · · · · · · · · · · ·

Little Fockers

· · · · · · · · · · · · · · · · · · ·

Beauty and the Beast

· · · · · · · · · · · · · · · · · · ·

The Fast and the Furious

· · · · · · · · · · · · · · · · · · ·

In & Out

· · · · · · · · · · · · · · · · · · ·

Buffy the Vampire Slayer

Knocked Up

There are two ways to go about miming the title of this raunchy comedy: the easy way and the hard way – or rather, the clean way and the dirty way. You could just go through, syllable by syllable, until you have a nice, easy win for your team. It would be far more fun, however, to mime the entire conception process, from first glance at a bar to weeing on your pregnancy test. Surely there should be points for style as well as accuracy in charades?

Chitty Chitty Bang Bang

. . . .

Blown Away

. . . .

The Happy Ending

. . . .

The 400 Blows

. . . .

Free Willy

. . . .

Let the Right One In

. . . .

The Harder They Come

. . . .

Hot Fuzz

That Thing You Do!

. . . .

Ride the Pink Horse

. . . .

Holes

. . . .

The Dirty Dozen

. . . .

Big

. . . .

Fire Down Below

. . . .

Love Actually

. . . .

Five Fingers

Octopussy

It's not like anyone has ever accused James Bond films of being good, clean fun but there's something especially disturbing about this movie title. What exactly is the eponymous character Octopussy implying? Does she have eight, ahem, you-know-whats? Or is she blessed with tentacles in unusual places, like some Lovecraftian pin-up? Have fun deciding your approach to this one!

*Willy Wonka and the
Chocolate Factory*

. . . .

Taken

. . . .

What Lies Beneath

. . . .

Freddy Got Fingered

. . . .

*Walk Hard:
The Dewey Cox Story*

. . . .

Splash

. . . .

Big Fish

The Bone Collector

. . . .

Big Momma's House

. . . .

Deep Impact

. . . .

Every Which Way But Loose

. . . .

Swingers

. . . .

There Will Be Blood

. . . .

Shaft

. . . .

Wee Willie Winkie

Hancock

. . . .

Rust and Bone

. . . .

Joy Ride

. . . .

The Pink Panther

. . . .

In Too Deep

. . . .

Big Daddy

. . . .

Blow

. . . .

Kiss Kiss Bang Bang

Raging Bull

. . . .

Ed Wood

. . . .

Easy Rider

. . . .

Failure to Launch

. . . .

Gone with the Wind

. . . .

Mission: Impossible

. . . .

Basic Instinct

. . . .

Some Like It Hot

Snatch

This one's a winner for all genders but particularly good for male participants. For women it can be a simple case of pointing and waiting on your team to hit on the right slang word but for men there's a certain amount of complication. Just how are they going to mime female genitals? Make it even funnier by establishing a 'no props or pointing to audience members' rule.

Private Parts

. . . .

Commando

. . . .

Easy A

. . . .

G-Force

. . . .

Gone in 60 Seconds

. . . .

Rita, Sue and Bob Too

. . . .

The Big Lebowski

. . . .

Blown Away

Kiss of the Spider Woman

. . . .

The Stepford Wives

. . . .

Barbarella

. . . .

Attack of the 50 Foot Woman

. . . .

The Untouchables

. . . .

Emmanuelle

. . . .

Eyes Wide Shut

. . . .

Bend It Like Beckham

The Wind Rises

· ·

Fatal Attraction

· ·

9½ Weeks

· ·

Spanking the Monkey

COCKTAILS

Mime taking a drink

Be honest, you've probably had a lot of practise for this section already, haven't you? We've all been there; approaching midnight in a packed bar, half-shouting, half-miming your request for a Slippery Nipple to a nonplussed bartender who either can't or won't understand you. It's time to dust off those cocktail-requesting skills, rehearse your best Screaming Orgasm face in the mirror and warm up your pelvis for a Slow Comfortable Screw. Let's hope your teammates get it faster than the bartenders do.

Sex on the Beach

. . . .

Gin and It

. . . .

Buttery Nipple

. . . .

Slippery Nipple

. . . .

Between the Sheets

. . . .

Screaming Orgasm

. . . .

Slow Comfortable Screw

. . . .

Deep Throat

Harvey Wallbanger

Who exactly was Harvey Wallbanger? Why did he have such a penchant for walls? The answers to these questions are lost in the mists of time and hangovers but the cocktail, thankfully, is not. It's made up of vodka, Galliano and orange juice, served in a highball glass. Sweet and tasty, not only is it a fun charades clue but it also could make a pretty fine refreshment after a heated round. Charades is thirsty work after all.

Bend Over Shirley

. . . .

Sex On My Face

. . . .

Pussy Paws

. . . .

Wet Panties

. . . .

Dr Pecker

. . . .

Ménage-à-Trois

. . . .

Cock-Sucking Cowboy

. . . .

The Leg Spreader

Blow Job

. . . .

Creamy Pussy

. . . .

Three-legged Monkey

. . . .

Tight Snatch

. . . .

Angel's Tit

. . . .

Red-headed Slut

. . . .

Pop My Cherry

Liquid Viagra

Liquid Viagra is a pretty bold cocktail name considering the, er, deflating effect alcohol is meant to have on your performance ability. Still, bright blue and containing both Curacao and Goldschläger, this one should perk up your spirits, if not your pecker. It's also a hard one – heh – only for expert-level players so good luck!

BOOKS

Hold out your hands together in front of you, then open them like a book

INTRODUCTION

Ah books, those dusty tomes that live in little bookshops, in libraries and on the floor of the bog. How could they be dirty when they're written by noble souls, such as Charles Dickens, Jane Austen and J. K. Rowling? I mean, there is *Moby Dick*. *Of Human Bondage* sounds pretty racy. And what was *The Secret Garden* all about again? Oh stuff it; those uptight writers are as obsessed with sex as the rest of us, slipping in innuendos all over the place, insinuating all sorts of goings on. Welcome to your very own lewd library of charade ideas.

The Secret Garden

. . . .

Westward Ho!

. . . .

Moby Dick

. . . .

The Golden Ass

. . . .

Scouts in Bondage

. . . .

Vanity Fair

. . . .

Dick Whittington

Norwegian Wood

. . . .

Middlesex

. . . .

Go the F**k to Sleep

. . . .

Sons and Lovers

. . . .

Of Human Bondage

. . . .

Winnie-the-Pooh

. . . .

Who Will Toss My Salad?

The Second Sex

No, not the name for those rare shall-we-go-again sessions, where, either impressed or disappointed by your first-stage lovemaking skills, you find it within yourself to gussy up for a second round, *The Second Sex* is instead a seminal feminist manifesto, written by seminal feminist human Simone de Beauvoir (no her last name is NOT French for beaver). See if you can get some of the weightiness of the original across while thrusting in the general direction of your charades team.

Memoirs of a Geisha

. . . .

The Black Stallion

. . . .

Dangerous Liaisons

. . . .

Diary of a Call Girl

. . . .

Keep Calm and Carry On

. . . .

The Lovely Bones

. . . .

Men Without Women

. . . .

The Pursuit of Love

How to Bonk at Work

. . . .

The Idiot

. . . .

The Master and Margarita

. . . .

Lady Chatterley's Lover

. . . .

Lolita

. . . .

Shag the Pony

. . . .

Delta of Venus

Naked Lunch

Naked Lunch, or Saturday as it's known in some households, is a pretty freaky surrealist jaunt filled with sex and drugs (this may still apply to your Saturday afternoon, no judgement here) by William S. Burroughs. How far you go in committing to miming this title is entirely up to you – and probably your audience too. They may be so overcome by horror or excitement that you never even get round to miming the lunch.

The 120 Days of Sodom

. . . .

Venus in Furs

. . . .

Hard Times

. . . .

The Virgin Suicides

. . . .

Fifty Shades of Grey

. . . .

Sex and the City

. . . .

Games You Can Play With Your Pussy

. . . .

High Fidelity

Everyone Poops

. . . .

Uncle Tom's Cabin

. . . .

Crime and Punishment

. . . .

Gone with the Wind

. . . .

Love in a Cold Climate

. . . .

Fanny by Gaslight

. . . .

The Age of Innocence

. . . .

Story of O

The Joy of Sex

. . . .

The Women's Room

. . . .

Lace

. . . .

Sexing the Cherry

. . . .

Oranges Are Not the Only Fruit

PLAYS AND MUSICALS

Go down on one knee and hold
your arms out in a flamboyant
gesture (think Shakespeare)

Watching a musical has been your lovely nan's favourite pastime for donkey's years, so you best hope she's never caught on to any of these naughty names. Or who knows, maybe she's disappointed when, on turning up hopefully to see *Fiddler on the Roof*, it really is just a heart-warming tale of a poor Jewish milkman and his daughters. If that's so, cheer her up by inviting her to a round of adult charades. Nothing warms a heart more than to see your grandchild attempt to mime the title of Eugene O' Neill's seminal 1939 play, *The Iceman Cometh*.

The Vagina Monologues

. . . .

Fiddler on the Roof

. . . .

A Streetcar Named Desire

. . . .

Oedipus the King

. . . .

Electra

. . . .

As You Like It

. . . .

Bent

. . . .

In the Boom Boom Room

'Tis Pity She's a Whore

When John Ford wrote *'Tis Pity She's a Whore* in the 1600s, he certainly wasn't interested in mincing words. One might assume that things were more strait-laced and uptight in those days but anyone who has sat through two hours of incest, murder and double-crossing would know differently. Hopefully your team guesses your miming attempt a little more quickly than that.

Sexual Perversity in Chicago

. . . .

Love! Valour! Compassion!

. . . .

The Member of the Wedding

. . . .

The Taming of the Shrew

. . . .

All's Well That Ends Well

. . . .

Ain't Misbehavin'

. . . .

Titus Andronicus

. . . .

The Playboy of the Western World

Kinky Boots

. . . .

The Ice Man Cometh

. . . .

Oh! Calcutta!

. . . .

Lysistrata

. . . .

A Midsummer Night's Dream

. . . .

The Cherry Orchard

. . . .

Lady Windermere's Fan

. . . .

Much Ado About Nothing

. . . .

The Elephant Man

An Ideal Husband

One thing is for certain; genius playwright, awful gossip, sly insinuator and author of *An Ideal Husband*, Oscar Wilde would utterly enjoy a game of adult charades. If all that dirty behaviour wasn't enough, there are always plenty of heated relationship moments brought on by competitive natures and long-standing grudges. No, I don't know why your hubby didn't get your perfectly legible miming of *The Vagina Monologues* but whatever you do don't point to someone else when it comes to *An Ideal Husband*.

SONGS

Move your hands outwards from your mouth, like an opera singer

INTRODUCTION

Finally! Now's the time to unleash all those moves hitherto seen only on a sweaty dance floor after more than a few drinks, or at 7 p.m. at your cousin's wedding reception (also after a few drinks). 'Sex Machine'? Nailed it. 'You Can Leave Your Hat On'? Bet you've practised that in front of the mirror more than once. 'I'm Too Sexy'? You just feel bad for the competition. Come on 'Wild Thing', 'Let's Get It On' and play some serious adult charades.

'Push It'

. . . .

'You Can Leave Your Hat On'

. . . .

'Glad You Came'

. . . .

'Air on a G-String'

. . . .

'Hit Me With Your Best Shot'

. . . .

'Sex Machine'

. . . .

'Come as You Are'

. . . .

'I'm Going Down'

'Slide It In'

. . . .

'My Neck, My Back (Lick It)'

. . . .

'Let's Stay Together'

. . . .

'Hold On, I'm Coming'

. . . .

'Hand in My Pocket'

. . . .

'I'm Too Sexy'

. . . .

'The Harder They Come'

'Come Together'

. . . .

'Knocking at Your Back Door'

. . . .

'Let's Get It On'

. . . .

'Love Machine'

. . . .

'Come on Eileen'

. . . .

'Get Up'

. . . .

'Love Gun'

'Great Balls of Fire'

Goodness gracious, what an expression. There's a certain delight to the exclamations of yesteryear; swearing is all very well but it's not as fun as reacting to a bit of bad news with 'Codswallop' or 'Great Scott'! It's certainly lots of fun to attempt to mime out this expression-cum-hit-song, as many, many embarrassing dads have proved at a family party.

'Whip It'

. . . .

'Let's Do It (Let's Fall in Love)'

. . . .

'Dirrty'

. . . .

'Ride the Pony'

. . . .

'More, More, More'

. . . .

'Wild'

. . . .

'It's Been a Long Time Coming'

. . . .

'How Deep Is Your Love'

'Good Vibrations'

. . . .

'Smack That'

. . . .

'Bang Bang'

. . . .

'Let's Spend the Night Together'

. . . .

'Sexual Healing'

. . . .

'Between the Sheets'

. . . .

'Do Ya Think I'm Sexy?'

. . . .

'Bad'

'You Shook Me All Night Long'

. . . .

'Love Shack'

. . . .

'Light My Fire'

. . . .

'Stairway to Heaven'

. . . .

'Rocket Man'

. . . .

'Tighten Up'

. . . .

'Oh, What a Night'

. . . .

'Work It'

. . . .

'La Bamba'

'Why Don't We Do It in the Road?'

. . . .

'Big Pimpin''

. . . .

'Don't Let the Sun Go Down on Me'

. . . .

'See Me, Feel Me'

. . . .

'Enter Sandman'

. . . .

'Fuck Her Gently'

. . . .

'Love Me Tender'

. . . .

'My Ding-A-Ling'

'Pearl Necklace'

What a charming song about giving your sweet girlfriend a present she requested – a truly loving display of generosity. Oh wait. Hang on, news just in. This is NOT a sweet song, this is a rude song! ZZ Top, beloved dad rockers, aren't talking about a lovely string of pearls at all. Or at least not pearls from an oyster, if you're picking up what I'm putting down. This could be a good naughty charade or a team effort, or perhaps it would be even funnier if one person acted both parts.

'Lady Marmalade *(Voulez-Vous Coucher Avec Moi?)*'

. . . .

'Boom Boom Boom Boom!! (I Want You In My Room)'

. . . .

'Bump 'n' Grind'

. . . .

'Let's Get Physical'

. . . .

'Family Affair'

. . . .

'Whole Lotta Love'

. . . .

'I Never Loved a Man'

'Please Please Me'

. . . .

'Satisfaction'

. . . .

'Hot Stuff'

. . . .

'Love in an Elevator'

. . . .

'Get Ur Freak On'

. . . .

'Like a Virgin'

. . . .

'Ring of Fire'

. . . .

'Let's Stick Together'

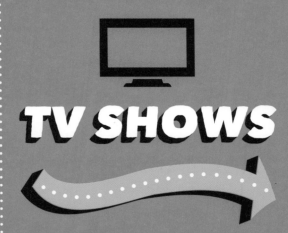

TV SHOWS

Describe a small rectangle in the air
with your forefingers

There really is an art to rude charades. There are the clearly filthy ideas, your *The Dick Tracy Show*s and your *Sex and the City*s. But there are also the subtle suggestions, the ideas that aren't so clearly rude until you start to mime out *Countryfile* and you realise that in order to get the first syllable it's go big or go home. In those cases it's time to make like Matt Baker, put on your big boy wellies and wade in; charades is no game for wimps.

Desperate Housewives

. . . .

The Rockford Files

. . . .

Flash Gordon

. . . .

Peep Show

. . . .

Sex and the City

. . . .

The Dick Tracy Show

. . . .

The Dick Van Dyke Show

. . . .

30 Rock

Twin Peaks

You know, every woman's breasts are asymmetrical, so in boob terms *Twin Peaks* isn't quite accurate. However, what the technically correct *Fraternal Twin Peaks* might gain in precision it loses in snappiness. There is no evidence that David Lynch meant to imply breasts when he was creating the hit nineties TV show but given the amount of naughty behaviour he packed in there, that was almost certainly his aim.

Hung

. . . .

Bones

. . . .

Diff'rent Strokes

. . . .

Brass Eye

. . . .

Happy Valley

. . . .

The Golden Girls

. . . .

Deadwood

. . . .

The Angry Beavers

Rude Tube

. . . .

Dragon Ball Z

. . . .

The Big Bang Theory

. . . .

Jane the Virgin

. . . .

Miami Vice

. . . .

I Love Lucy

. . . .

Sex Box

. . . .

Embarrassing Bodies

Poker After Dark

Poker After Dark, but only if she's into that. You never know, she might be more of a morning person. Being successful at poker is all about strength of mind, concentration, endurance and quick reaction times. Of course, being successful at poking requires many of the same skills. See if you have the skills to pull off this cheeky charade; two players optional.

The Box of Delights

. . . .

Countryfile

. . . .

Location, Location, Location

. . . .

Metal Mickey

. . . .

Skins

. . . .

Bagpuss

. . . .

Dixon of Dock Green

. . . .

Trumpton

FOOD

Mime eating with a knife and fork

Some might say that the Brits have a bit of a stick up their whatsit, but one only has to look at some of their finest national dishes to know that this isn't the case. Battered sausage, spotted dick, toad-in-the-hole; clearly there's one thing on the average British chef's mind. That's without even getting started on the fantastically, bafflingly named knickerbocker glory or Sunday favourite, stuffed turkey. It's surprising that one can get through a meal of good old British grub without feeling a little tingly!

Chicken balls

. . . .

Cock soup

. . . .

Cock-a-leekie soup

. . . .

Buttered crumpet

. . . .

Spit-roasted bird

. . . .

Spotted dick

. . . .

Knickerbocker glory

. . . .

Toad in the Hole

Kumquat

For those who may not have come across this provocatively named fruit, I can assure you it's real. Although it sounds like a sex move you only read about on Urban Dictionary, it's actually a little citrus fruit from South Asia. The plant symbolises luck in China and other Asian countries, so don't be alarmed if a neighbour offers to give you a lucky kumquat – it's all in good taste.

French tart

. . . .

Battered sausage

. . . .

Chicken breast

. . . .

Stuffed turkey

. . . .

Rump steak

. . . .

Dumplings

. . . .

Firm melons

. . . .

Juicy pears

Meat and two veg

· · · · · · · · · · · · · · · · · · · ·

Devils on horseback

· · · · · · · · · · · · · · · · · · · ·

Roly-poly pudding

· · · · · · · · · · · · · · · · · · · ·

Suckling pig

· · · · · · · · · · · · · · · · · · · ·

Bamboo shoots

· · · · · · · · · · · · · · · · · · · ·

Coq au vin

· · · · · · · · · · · · · · · · · · · ·

Warm muffin

· · · · · · · · · · · · · · · · · · · ·

Hot sauce

Tossed salad

How salad – the most boring of assembled foods – became a euphemism for a reasonably daring sex act isn't clear. If the two were to be equivalent, the sex act named after salad should be a little light hand holding. At most, if it were a particularly exciting salad with croutons and a little drizzle, it could be considered a little neck kissing. But hey, who am I to judge the slang terms for annilingus?

Blue cheese

. . . .

Eton mess

. . . .

Saucy meatballs

. . . .

Cream pie

. . . .

Bubble and squeak

. . . .

Head cheese

. . . .

White sauce

SPORT

Act out hitting a ball with a bat

How you interpret these saucy sporting charades is completely up to you, although for the sake of team spirit and morale it may be best to not take fartlek too literally. Between the vuvuzela, games of keepie-uppie and a long ball, it may initially seem that football is the rudest sport of all. But then that would be discounting the hookers of rugby or all those shafts in ice hockey.

FOOTBALL

Dribbling

Flat back four

Game of two halves

Hand of God

Playing away

Keepie-uppie

Long ball

Magic sponge

Nutmeg

Open goal

Parking the bus

Pitch invasion

Offside rule

Shooter

Five-a-side

Toss-up

Yellow card

Red card

Three-match ban

Suspension

Vuvuzela

Foul play

One man down

Ball games

Back pass

Bung

Handball

RUGBY UNION

Hand-off

Hooker

Spear tackle

Tight head

Loose head

Touch judge

Uncontested scrum

Up and under

Sin bin

Jockstrap

ICE HOCKEY

Two-man advantage

Biscuit in the basket

Butt-ending

Check to the head

Crashing the net

Goal suck

Hockey grinder

Offensive zone

The referee's crease

Shaft (of the stick)

Stick handling

Throwing your stick

ATHLETICS

Crouch start

Fartlek

Fosbury Flop

Baton

Javelin

Pole vault

Steeplechase

Triple Jump

SWIMMING

Stroke length

Freestyle

Breast stroke

Public health warning: only your own breasts should be stroked in the performing of this charade. I repeat: this is no occasion to make a lunge for the nearest pair of boobs, unless the owner of those boobs has previously made it clear that they are down for some in-public stroking. And if you don't have any breasts of your own – tough! Time to mime some – it will only make it more hilarious.

Judges of stroke

Finish judges

Drag suit

Hand paddles

Back shot

Knock in

Mallet head

Pony goal

ROCK CLIMBING

Soloing

Flash

Rack

Headpoint

HORSE RIDING

Bareback riding

Riding sidesaddle

Nosebag

Furlong

Stable hand

Four-in-hand

It's an ambitious person who attempts a four-in-hand, whether while horse riding, during charades or just in their private life. Still, what is life for if not for taking risks? Whether you'll be allowed to use two hands entirely depends on your teammates and whether you have any keen riders in the audience – they may be sticklers for the rules.

Stallion

Stud book

Getting a leg over

CRICKET

Wicket keeper

Bowl a maiden over

Half-cocked

SNOOKER

Screw back

Sink the pink

Pot the brown